Master KS2 Reading with CGP!

When it comes to reading in Year 4, practice makes perfect. That's why CGP have made this indispensable Question Book!

It's full of fascinating texts by a variety of authors — each with practice questions to check pupils' understanding and deepen their knowledge of techniques used by authors.

We've even included helpful answers at the back of the book.

What CGP is all about

Our sole aim here at CGP is to produce the highest quality books — carefully written, immaculately presented and dangerously close to being funny.

Then we work our socks off to get them out to you — at the cheapest possible prices.

Contents

Published by CGP

Anthologist: Christopher Edge
Questions written by Amanda MacNaughton
Consultant: Julie Docker
Reviewers: Sam Bensted, Juliette Green, Maxine Petrie
Editors: Melissa Gardner, Kelsey Hammond, Christopher Lindle, Sam Norman, Gabrielle Richardson, Rosa Roberts

With thanks to Izzy Bowen, Alison Griffin, Sophie Herring and Holly Robinson for the proofreading.
With thanks to Ana Pungartnik for the copyright research.

ISBN: 978 1 78908 357 6

Printed by Elanders Ltd, Newcastle upon Tyne.

About this Book

This book consists of nine stimulating texts for pupils to read, with two sets of questions for each text:

- Question Set 1 checks that pupils understand the text as a whole, with lots of retrieval questions.
- Question Set 2 gets pupils thinking more deeply, with more questions requiring inference.

Question Pages

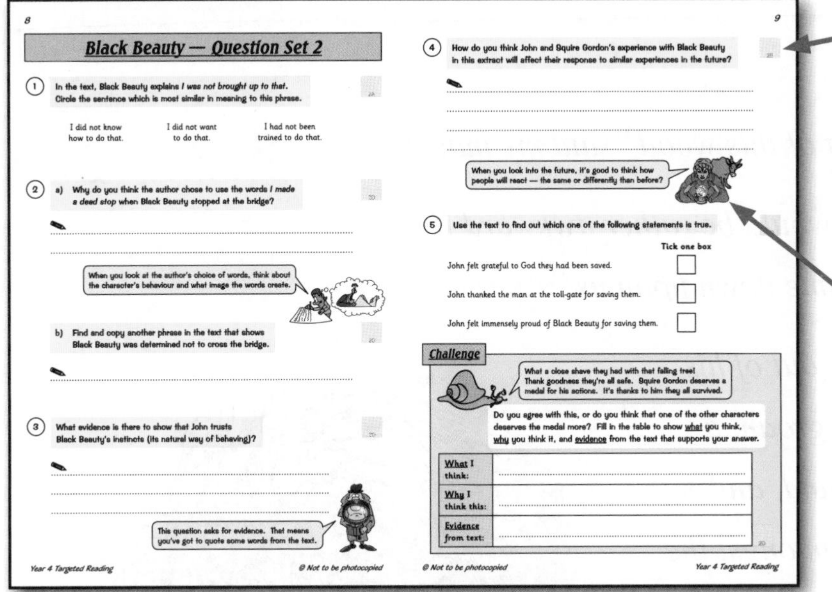
8

Black Beauty — Question Set 2

1. In the text, Black Beauty explains *I was not brought up to that.* Circle the sentence which is most similar in meaning to this phrase.

   I did not know how to do that. | I did not want to do that. | I had not been trained to do that.

2. a) Why do you think the author chose to use the words *I made a dead stop* when Black Beauty stopped at the bridge?

   When you look at the author's choice of words, think about the character's behaviour and what image the words create.

   b) Find and copy another phrase in the text that shows Black Beauty was determined not to cross the bridge.

3. What evidence is there to show that John trusts Black Beauty's instincts (its natural way of behaving)?

   This question asks for evidence. That means you've got to quote some words from the text.

Year 4 Targeted Reading — © Not to be photocopied

9

4. How do you think John and Squire Gordon's experience with Black Beauty in this extract will affect their response to similar experiences in the future?

   When you look into the future, it's good to think how people will react — the same or differently than before?

5. Use the text to find out which one of the following statements is true.

   Tick one box

   John felt grateful to God they had been saved. ☐

   John thanked the man at the toll-gate for saving them. ☐

   John felt immensely proud of Black Beauty for saving them. ☐

Challenge

What a close shave they had with that falling tree! Thank goodness they're all safe. Squire Gordon deserves a medal for his actions. It's thanks to him they all survived.

Do you agree with this, or do you think that one of the other characters deserves the medal more? Fill in the table to show what you think, why you think it, and evidence from the text that supports your answer.

What I think:	
Why I think this:	
Evidence from text:	

© Not to be photocopied — Year 4 Targeted Reading

The mark boxes give the national curriculum content area for the question: 2B

Pupils are given tips on how to tackle some questions.

The recurring characters familiarise pupils with different types of question:

Scanning the text

Finding evidence in the text

National Curriculum References

Here is a key to the national curriculum references for the different question types:

- 2A give / explain the meaning of words in context
- 2B retrieve and record information / identify key details from fiction and non-fiction
- 2C summarise main ideas from more than one paragraph
- 2D make inferences from the text / explain and justify inferences with evidence from the text
- 2E predict what might happen from details stated and implied
- 2F identify / explain how information / narrative content is related and contributes to meaning as a whole
- 2G identify / explain how meaning is enhanced through choice of words and phrases
- 2H make comparisons within the text

At the back of the book, you'll find a table where you can record the pupil's performance in the different content areas:

		National Curriculum Content Areas							
		2a Word Meaning	2b Retrieval	2c Summarising	2d Inference	2e Prediction	2f Text Meaning	2g Language	2h Comparison
Text 1: Black Beauty	Set 1	Q5	Q1 Q2 Q3 Q4	Q6					
	Set 2	Q1			Q2 Q3 Q5 Ch	Q4			
Text 2: Pheasant's Revolt	Set 1	Q5	Q1 Q2 Q3a Q4	Q6					Q3b
	Set 2	Q3	Q5		Q2 Q4 Ch			Q1	
Text 3: Gregor and the Curse of the Warmbloods	Set 1	Q3	Q1 Q2	Q5				Q4 Q6	
	Set 2		Q1 Q4		Q3 Q5 Ch	Q2a			Q2b

Black Beauty

Start reading here. There might be important information in the introduction.

The novel *Black Beauty* by Anna Sewell was first published in 1877. This story is told by a horse named Black Beauty. Here, Black Beauty is pulling his master, Squire Gordon, and his groom, John, in a carriage on a stormy night.

"I wish we were well out of this wood," said my master.

"Yes, sir," said John, "it would be rather awkward if one of these branches came down upon us."

The words were scarcely out of his mouth when there was a groan, a crack, and a splitting sound, and tearing, crashing down amongst the other trees, came an oak, torn up by the roots, which fell right across the road just before us. I will never say I was not frightened, for I was. I stopped still, and I believe I trembled. Of course I did not turn round or run away; I was not brought up to that. John jumped out and in a moment was at my head.

"That was a very near touch," said my master. "What's to be done now?"

"Well, sir, we can't drive over that tree nor yet get round it; there will be nothing for it but to go back to the four crossways, and that will be a good six miles before we get round to the wooden bridge again. It will make us late, but the horse is fresh."

So back we went, and round by the crossroads; but by the time we got to the bridge it was very nearly dark, and we could just see that the water was over the middle of it; but as that happened sometimes when the floods were out, master did not stop.

We were going along at a good pace, but the moment my feet touched the first part of the bridge, I felt sure there was something wrong. I dare not go forward, and so I made a dead stop. "Go on, Beauty," said my master, giving me a touch with the whip, but I dare not stir. He gave me a sharp cut; I jumped, but I dared not go forward.

"There's something wrong, sir," said John; and he sprang out of the dog-cart and came to my head and looked all about. He tried to lead me forward. "Come on, Beauty, what's the matter?" Of course I could not tell him, but I knew very well that the bridge was not safe.

Just then the man at the toll-gate on the other side ran out of the house, tossing a torch about like one mad.

"Hoy, hoy, hoy, halloo, stop!" he cried.

"What's the matter?" shouted my master.

"The bridge is broken in the middle, and part of it is carried away; if you come on you'll be into the river."

"Thank God!" said my master. "You Beauty!" said John.

An extract from *Black Beauty* by Anna Sewell.

Consider

Imagine that Black Beauty hadn't known that something was wrong with the bridge and the group had begun to cross it. What do you think would have happened to them?

Black Beauty — Question Set 1

1. **Draw lines to match the character's name to their part in this story.** 2B

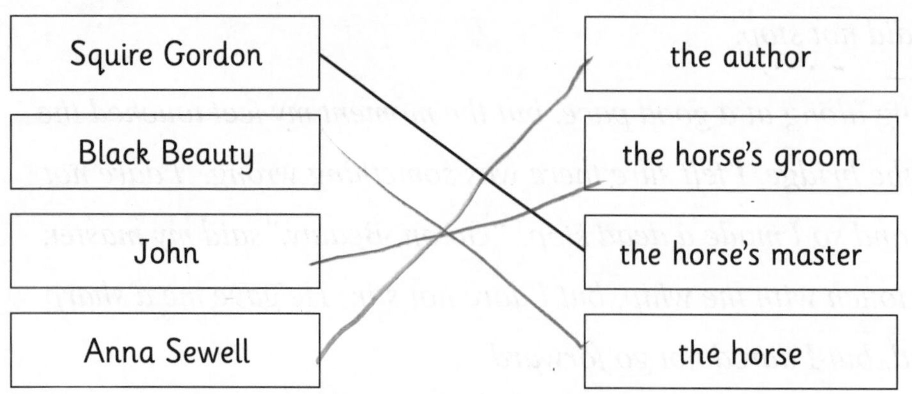

2. **Who or what made *a groan, a crack, and a splitting sound*?** 2B

The oak tree

> **In this question the words '*a groan, a crack, and a splitting sound*' are a quote from the text. You'll need to scan the text for these exact words.**

3. **Read these statements carefully and decide if they are true or false.** 2B

	True	False
Black Beauty was frightened by the tree falling.		
Squire Gordon stood by Black Beauty to comfort him.		
They decided to continue on their journey by travelling around the oak tree.		
Black Beauty knew something was wrong before he stepped on the bridge.		
The man waving a torch at them and shouting was on the other side of the bridge.		

4 **In what two ways do the men try to encourage Black Beauty to cross the bridge?**

2B

1. whip him with a stick.

2. give him a cut

5 **What does the man at the toll-gate mean when he says *part of it is carried away?***

2A

some part of the bridge has broken of and floated away

When you have to work out the meaning, read around the words (the context) to help you work it out.

6 **Put these events from the story in the order in which they happened.**

2C

They turn around and go back the way they came.	3
They are informed of the broken bridge.	5
The small group are travelling through the woods.	1
Sensing danger, Black Beauty refuses to cross the bridge.	4
A large oak tree crashes to the ground in front of them.	2

When you have to put events in order, it's like having to find a secret code. First find each of the five events in the story and underline them in the text. Then number the events in the text in the order they appear. Lastly, match each event in the question to the numbered event in the text.

Black Beauty — Question Set 2

(1) **In the text, Black Beauty explains *I was not brought up to that*. Circle the sentence which is most similar in meaning to this phrase.** 2A

I did not know how to do that. | I did not want to do that. | I had not been trained to do that. (circled)

(2) **a) Why do you think the author chose to use the words *I made a dead stop* when Black Beauty stopped at the bridge?** 2D

because Black Beaty stopped immidetly

When you look at the author's choice of words, think about the character's behaviour and what image the words create.

b) Find and copy another phrase in the text that shows Black Beauty was determined not to cross the bridge. 2D

dared not to

(3) **What evidence is there to show that John trusts Black Beauty's instincts (its natural way of behaving)?** 2D

There's something wrong sir because the horse doesn't stop unless somethings wrong

This question asks for evidence. That means you've got to quote some words from the text.

(4) How do you think John and Squire Gordon's experience with Black Beauty in this extract will affect their response to similar experiences in the future? 2E

Always listen to Black Beauty. because he knows what's right

When you look into the future, it's good to think how people will react — the same or differently than before?

(5) Use the text to find out which one of the following statements is true. 2D

	Tick one box
John felt grateful to God they had been saved.	☐
John thanked the man at the toll-gate for saving them.	☐
John felt immensely proud of Black Beauty for saving them.	☑

Challenge

What a close shave they had with that falling tree! Thank goodness they're all safe. Squire Gordon deserves a medal for his actions. It's thanks to him they all survived.

Do you agree with this, or do you think that one of the other characters deserves the medal more? Fill in the table to show what you think, why you think it, and evidence from the text that supports your answer.

What I think:	
Why I think this:	
Evidence from text:	

2D

Pheasant's Revolt

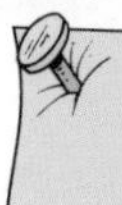

Newspapers inform their readers about the most important stories in the news, but they also report on more unusual or funny events too. The following report is about a wild pheasant who is attacking the people who live on a street in a village called Costessey.

PHEASANT'S REVOLT

Fiery Phil the pheasant forces residents to stay in their homes after biting and chasing after them.

By Rob Pattinson and Adam Bennett

A fiery pheasant is terrorising a whole street — biting and clawing residents, chasing pets and chewing car wipers.

The angry bird, dubbed Phil, pecks at windows looking for a fight and waits for locals to leave their homes before pouncing.

POSTIES IN PERIL

Postmen have resorted to squirting vinegar spray to fend him off after high-pitched sensors and gun noises failed to work.

Others shoo him away with umbrellas.

Businessman Matt Cheetham, 42, whose home is next to woods in Costessey, Norfolk, said: "Forget The Terminator, this bird is The Termi-nester. He just seems unstoppable."

"My wife tried to drive off but it jumped on the bonnet and pecked at the wipers. She can only leave the house with me so I can shield her."

Phil has attacked daily since December 23, catching residents and visitors at least four times.

One postman said: "This bird is lethal. A colleague got a nasty scratch on his face. We're all scared."

VELOCIRAPTOR

Another victim, Sonya Bolton, 28, added: "Phil is like a velociraptor. Only yesterday he was pinning the postman up against our door."

Resident Shahin Assadinia, 39, now carries an umbrella to protect himself from the pesky pheasant.

The university lecturer said: "He's really getting on my nerves now. He pecks at my feet when he sees me, so much so that I am carrying an umbrella with me to protect myself."

"I think that he thinks we are on his territory and that's why he's getting aggressive."

NOTHING TO BE DONE

There's no end in sight to Phil's acts of terror, with police and council chiefs saying they can do nothing.

Animal charities say they can intervene only if an animal is in danger.

The RSPB said: "If the bird is coming into maturity it will be trying to establish a pecking order with his territory, where the houses are."

The RSPCA added: "There's not much the postman can do other than stay out of the pheasant's way."

Glossary

RSPCA — Royal Society for the Prevention against Cruelty to Animals

RSPB — Royal Society for the Protection of Birds

Discuss

Find three things that Fiery Phil has been doing which have annoyed the residents. Compare your answers with a partner.

Pheasant's Revolt — Question Set 1

1 **Read the text carefully and decide if the following statements are true or false.** 2B

	True	False
The pheasant has been hurting the residents.	☐	☐
The residents have been feeding the pheasant.	☐	☐
The pheasant has jumped on to cars in the street.	☐	☐
The pheasant leaves the postmen alone.	☐	☐
Umbrellas are being used as defensive weapons.	☐	☐

2 **Which one of the following features is used in the sentence under the headline? Circle one answer.** 2B

a simile   an exclamation mark   alliteration

3 a) **Write down three different ways postmen have tried to get rid of the pheasant.** 2B

1. ....

2. ....

3. ....

When you are scanning the text for answers, it is important to start at the beginning of the text, not half way through.

b) **Which of the ways that you gave in part a) do you think is the best? Give a reason to support your answer.** 2H

....

....

4 **Draw lines to match the description of the pheasant (on the left) to the person or people who used the description (on the right).** 2B

Description	Person or people
The Termi-nester	the university lecturer
like a velociraptor	a postman
lethal	a local businessman
aggressive	the RSPB
trying to establish a pecking order	Sonya Bolton

5 ***A fiery pheasant is terrorising a whole street — biting and clawing residents, chasing pets and chewing car wipers.***
Circle the word below which could not replace *terrorising* in this sentence. 2A

persecuting delighting tormenting intimidating petrifying

Try putting each of the words into the sentence and see which one changes the meaning of the sentence.

6 **Imagine somebody new is moving into the street.**
Give them one piece of advice so they are prepared for Phil the pheasant. Use evidence from the text to support your answer. 2C

My advice:	....
Evidence from the text:	....

Be selective. What is the most important information they need to know?

Pheasant's Revolt — Question Set 2

1 Find and copy two phrases in the text which show the effect the pheasant's attacks are having on the residents. 2G

1. ....

2. ....

Remember — a phrase is a group of words. You'll need to copy the phrases carefully from the text.

2 Read the following information about velociraptors. 2D

The word velociraptor means 'speedy thief'. These scavengers had large brains and were very agile and fearsome predators. Their powerful back legs had long, sharp claws which would be lifted up when they were running and could rip into their prey. With their long, strong tails and front legs to grip prey, it would have been almost impossible to escape from their attack.

Why do you think Sonya Bolton chose to describe Phil the pheasant as being *like a velociraptor*?

....

....

....

3 What do you think Shahin Assadinia mean when he says *he thinks we are on his territory*? 2A

....

....

4 The RSPB and RSPCA *can intervene only if an animal is in danger.*
How would you convince the RSPB and the RSPCA that they must intervene? Write down two things you think the RSPB or RSPCA should do, and why.

2D

Action needed:	Reason why they should intervene:
1.	....
2.	....

5 **Phil is described as *fiery* and *angry*.**
Give three things he does to show his anger?

When you are asked to write what something or someone does, you'll be looking for verbs (action words).

Dictionary

2B

1. ....

2. ....

3. ....

Challenge

Gosh! These people aren't being very kind to poor Phil. Maybe they don't like animals at all. I'm sure Phil doesn't mean any harm — he's just trying to make friends with them.

Do you agree? Do you think the people should try harder to befriend Phil? Give one reason using evidence from the text to support your answer.

....

....

....

2D

Gregor and the Curse of the Warmbloods

Remember to read the introduction. It might contain important information.

The following extract is taken from a fantasy children's novel by Suzanne Collins. It takes place in an imaginary underground jungle.

Gregor's flashlight batteries died just as he was getting his lantern lit. Much to his surprise, he could still see! Not very well, not as if he were in daylight. But well enough to make out the silhouettes of the individual vines around him. Although the campfire had been extinguished, his flashlight was off, and the lanterns were unlit, the entire jungle was visible. He set the lanterns down and went to investigate. What was the source of light? It seemed to emanate from the ground itself. It grew fainter higher up, then dissolved into blackness about twelve feet in the air.

He moved to a spot where the light seemed strongest and found a narrow but deep stream. Along the bed, flashes of light came and went. He had seen something like this before in the crawlers' land — a stream with small volcanic eruptions on the bottom — but the bursts weren't as large or explosive as the ones before him. Gregor dipped his fingers in the stream and felt the warm water roll over them.

"There are hundreds of those streams crisscrossing the jungle," he heard Ripred say behind him. "Don't step in them, don't drink from them, and try not to use your fingers for bait."

Gregor jerked his hand out of the water as a set of spiky teeth snapped together in the space his fingers had just occupied. "What was that?" he asked, stepping back from the stream.

"Something that thinks you're yummy," said Ripred.

"Is that why we can't drink from them? It's too dangerous to get water?" asked Gregor.

"No, the water's tainted. Drink it and you die," said Ripred.

Gregor immediately went back and explained to Temp how scary the streams were so the cockroach would know to keep Boots clear of them. "Stream bad," agreed Temp.

But when Gregor told Boots to stay out of the water, she looked around eagerly and took off for the stream squealing, "Water? We go swimming?"

He chased after her and caught her by the arm. "No! No swimming! Bad water, Boots! You-don't-touch-water!" He said this so sharply that the sides of her mouth pointed down and her eyes filled with tears. "Hey, hey, it's okay. Don't cry." He hugged her. "Just stay away from the water here, okay? It's... it's too hot," he said. "Like in the bath?"

This seemed to make more sense to her. When the oil heater worked in their building, sometimes scalding water came from the tap.

"Ow?" she said,

"Right. Ow". He picked her up and carried her back to the others.

An extract from *Gregor and the Curse of the Warmbloods* by Suzanne Collins.

Discuss

Do you think an underground jungle is a good setting for a story set in an imaginary world? Discuss your ideas with a partner.

Gregor and the Curse of the Warmbloods — Question Set 1

1. **Give two reasons why Gregor is surprised that he can still see the jungle.** 2B

1. ....

2. ....

2. **What is different about the flashes of light and the eruptions in the stream compared to the ones Gregor had seen before?** 2B

....

....

Be careful with this question. The story says '... as the ones before him'. This means '... as the ones in front of him.'

3. **Draw lines to match the words from the text (on the left) with the word or phrase that could best replace them (on the right).** 2A

emanate	disappeared
dissolved	polluted
tainted	food
bait	spread out

Try replacing the word from the text with each word on the right — which one makes most sense?

4 **Find and copy the phrase in the text that suggests that there are lots of streams all over the jungle.** 2G

....

....

A phrase is a group of words. You need to copy them carefully when you write your answer.

5 **Number these events in the order they happen in the extract. One has been done for you.** 2C

Ripred warns Gregor of the dangers of the stream.	
Boots remembers being hurt by hot water before.	
Gregor is confused about where the light is coming from.	
Gregor is concerned for Temp and Boots's safety.	3
Boots becomes upset at the way Gregor speaks.	

First find and underline each event in the text. Number the events in the order they happen in the text. Then match each event in the question with the number you've written in the text.

6 **Why does the author use exclamation marks after the words *No!* and *No swimming!*?** 2G

....

....

Gregor and the Curse of the Warmbloods — Question Set 2

1. **What two things stop Gregor from exploring the stream any further?** 2B

1\. ....

....

2\. ....

....

Who? What? Where? When? Why?

Find evidence in the text from when Gregor is dipping his fingers in the stream.

2. a) **If the group continues to explore the jungle and decides to choose a leader, who do you think would be the best leader? Circle your choice.** 2E

Gregor   Ripred   Temp   Boots

b) **Why have you chosen this character?** 2H

....

....

....

Use the text to help you support your answer.

3. **Why do you think Boots runs towards the stream even though Gregor has told her to stay away from the water?** 2D

....

....

....

4 **Gregor speaks *sharply* the second time he tells Boots not to go in the water. What is the effect of the way he speaks?** 2B

Tick one box

Boots becomes cross with him.	☐
Boots runs excitedly towards the water.	☐
Boots becomes upset.	☐
Boots jumps into Gregor's arms in fright.	☐

5 **Which word in the text shows that Boots has experienced something bad to do with hot water in the past?** 2D

....

Challenge

If I'd been there I would have had a drink from the stream to cool me down in the hot jungle.

Would you have drunk from the stream? Circle one of the answers below. In the table, give a reason and some evidence from the text to support your answer.

I would have drunk from the stream.

I would not have drunk from the stream.

Reason:	....
Evidence from text:	....

2D

The Brilliance of Bees

Did you know that to make just one jar of honey, bees have to visit two million flowers and fly 88,000 km? That's more than twice the distance around the Earth. Making honey is pretty amazing, but that's not all bees do for us...

The Brilliance of Bees

How do bees make honey?

Honey is made from the nectar that female honey bees collect from flowers. The bee sucks the sugary liquid up through her long straw-like tongue and stores it in her 'honey stomach'. It's hard work collecting nectar, but luckily, if the bee gets hungry, she can open a valve in her honey stomach so that some of the nectar goes into her own stomach, giving her energy.

When her honey stomach is full she heads back to the hive and delivers the nectar to the honey-making bees in the hive. These bees chew on the nectar and pass it between themselves, mouth-to-mouth. The nectar gets drier and becomes honey. It's put into the hexagonal cells of honeycomb and sealed with a layer of beeswax to keep it fresh. It's like having rows and rows of storage jars!

If the honey isn't dry and sticky enough when it's put in the honeycomb cells, the bees fan it with their wings until it's just right.

Did you know?

A bee can carry almost her own weight in nectar. That's like you carrying 260 apples around!

Fantastic Fact

When a bee finds a great place to collect nectar, she tells the other bees where to find it by doing a 'waggle dance'. Her dance moves communicate the direction of the flowers, as well as how far away they are.

Why do bees make honey?

You might be thinking how kind bees are making all this delicious honey for us to eat, but that's not really why they do it. They make it so that the colony has food to eat over winter. The bees make much more honey than they need, so they don't miss it when some is removed by the beekeeper.

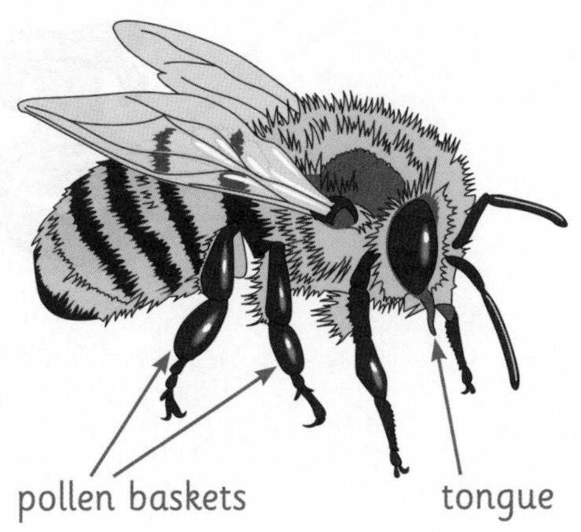

Bees collect pollen too!

Pollen is a powdery substance that parts of the flower produce. Bees store it in special structures on their back legs called pollen baskets. Back in the hive, the pollen grains are mixed with nectar and water to produce bee bread! Yum. This is the perfect food for baby bees in the bee nursery.

Honey bees need our help

Bees are in trouble! Pollution and climate change are two reasons why colonies are disappearing fast. It's a big problem, and not just because honey is delicious. As bees move from flower to flower, they move pollen about. This is called pollination and needs to happen for seeds to be produced — and without seeds, there'd be no fruit and no new plants. Bees do most of the pollination in the world, and without them humans would struggle to get enough to eat.

You can help honey bees by planting flowers and herbs such as bluebells, rosemary and chives in your garden. Letting grass grow long is good too, as it gives bees shelter.

Written by Sharon Keeley-Holden

Discuss

What has impressed you most about bees from what you've read in this text? Compare your thoughts with a partner.

The Brilliance of Bees — Question Set 1

1. **Which of the following things do bees have to do just to make one jar of honey?** 2B

Tick all that apply

fly twice around the world ☐

visit two million flowers ☐

carry 260 apples around ☐

fly 88,000 km ☐

Don't forget to read the introductory paragraph!

2. **When the nectar is collected from the flowers, what state is it in? Circle the correct answer.** 2B

solid liquid gas

3. **Number the following statements about how bees make honey to put them in the correct order. The first one has been done for you.** 2C

The nectar becomes honey and is stored in the honeycomb. ☐

The female honey bee returns to the hive. ☐

A layer of beeswax is used to seal the honeycomb. ☐

The honey-making bees chew the nectar to make it dry. ☐

The nectar is sucked up into the bee's honey stomach. 1

Time to find the secret code! Find and underline each of these events in the text. Number the events in the order they happen in the text. Then match each event in the question with the number you've written in the text.

4 **Look at the paragraph that begins *You might be thinking...* Find and copy a word from this paragraph that suggests the honey is tasty.** 2A

....

Scan the paragraph for a word which means tasty. The question has been kind and told you where to start looking.

5 ***They make it so that the colony has food to eat over winter.* Which of the following is the correct meaning of the word colony?** 2A

	Tick one box
babies	☐
people who like honey	☐
large group of animals living together	☐

6 **Draw lines to match the first half of each sentence (on the left) with the correct second half (on the right). Use the text to help you.** 2B

Long grass helps	nectar and water are mixed with pollen grains.
Pollen is moved when	to give bees shelter.
Bee bread is made when	to help keep the honey fresh.
A layer of beeswax is used	bees fly from flower to flower.

The Brilliance of Bees — Question Set 2

1) Look at the additional information in the sections on page 22 that start *A bee can carry...* and *If the honey...* . Explain what one of these sections is about. 2C

....

....

....

This question is asking you to summarise.
Re-read the information boxes, and explain the overall meaning of one of them in your own words.

2) Why do you think the 'honey stomach' is given this name? 2A

....

....

3) Do you think a 'waggle dance' is a good idea? Why or why not? 2D

....

....

....

....

Read the paragraph about the 'waggle dance'.
Make sure you have a reason for your thinking.

4 Look at the paragraph entitled *Bees collect pollen too!* How can you tell that the author thinks what the bees do is remarkable? 2G

....

....

What adjectives does the author use to show the bees are impressive?

5 a) If you wanted to read about the trouble bees are in, which section of the writing should you go to? 2C

....

b) What text feature has the author used to help the reader know what is being written about? Circle your answer. 2F

italic handwriting   capital letters   subheadings   contents page

Challenge

I don't like bees. They can sting dogs and don't do anything useful!

Explain why bees are useful and why we all depend on them. Use the text to justify your answer.

....

....

....

....

....

2D

Refrigerators

Explanation texts can help you understand how things work. The following extract explains how a refrigerator stays cool to keep the food inside fresh.

A refrigerator is a very important machine because keeping food cold stops it from going off. Normally you never see the back of a fridge, but the diagram opposite shows what's happening round the back.

A fridge works by taking heat from the inside compartment and carrying it to the outside. It does this by continuously pumping a special fluid, called a refrigerant, through a long loop of piping. On its journey, the refrigerant changes from a liquid into a **vapour**, and back to a liquid. As it becomes a vapour, the fridge absorbs heat from the food. When it turns back into a liquid, it releases the heat into the kitchen.

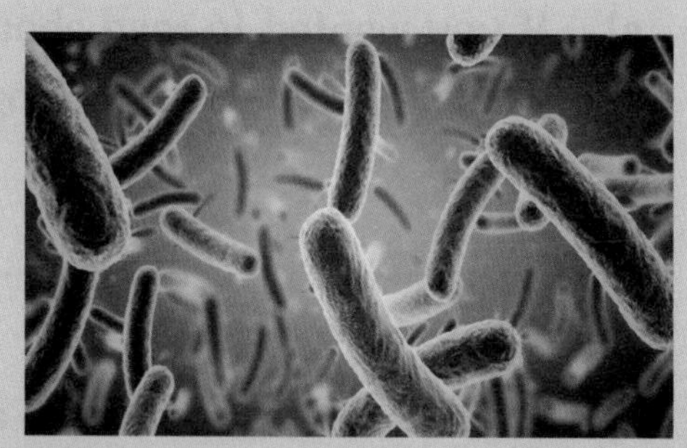

BAD NEWS FOR GERMS

All food has some germs on it. In warm conditions, these germs grow quickly and can make food go off. In a cool fridge they grow more slowly, so food stays fresh for longer.

1. KEEPING COOL

If you go for a swim and then come out without drying off, you'll soon start to feel cold. This is because the water on your skin, warmed by your body, starts to **evaporate** (turn to vapour) and takes heat away from you. In the same way, a fridge becomes cold as the heat from inside it turns liquid refrigerant into vapour.

2. INTO THE INTERIOR

When the refrigerant enters the fridge, it moves through a narrow **nozzle** or expansion valve into a series of pipes. Inside these pipes, the liquid refrigerant absorbs any heat from inside the fridge, and expands into a vapour. The fridge cools down, and its contents become very cold.

3. BACK TO THE COMPRESSOR

The refrigerant then flows down to the bottom of the fridge, carrying heat absorbed from the food. It enters the **compressor** (a small pump), which applies **pressure** to the vaporized refrigerant. The refrigerant is squeezed back into liquid form, and begins to release heat.

4. HEAT LOSS

After passing through the compressor, the refrigerant zigzags its way across the back of the fridge. During this part of its journey, pressure from the compressor continues to turn the vaporized refrigerant into a liquid. This releases the heat that was absorbed in the fridge. The heat travels away from the pipe, through metal rods, and escapes into the air outside the fridge.

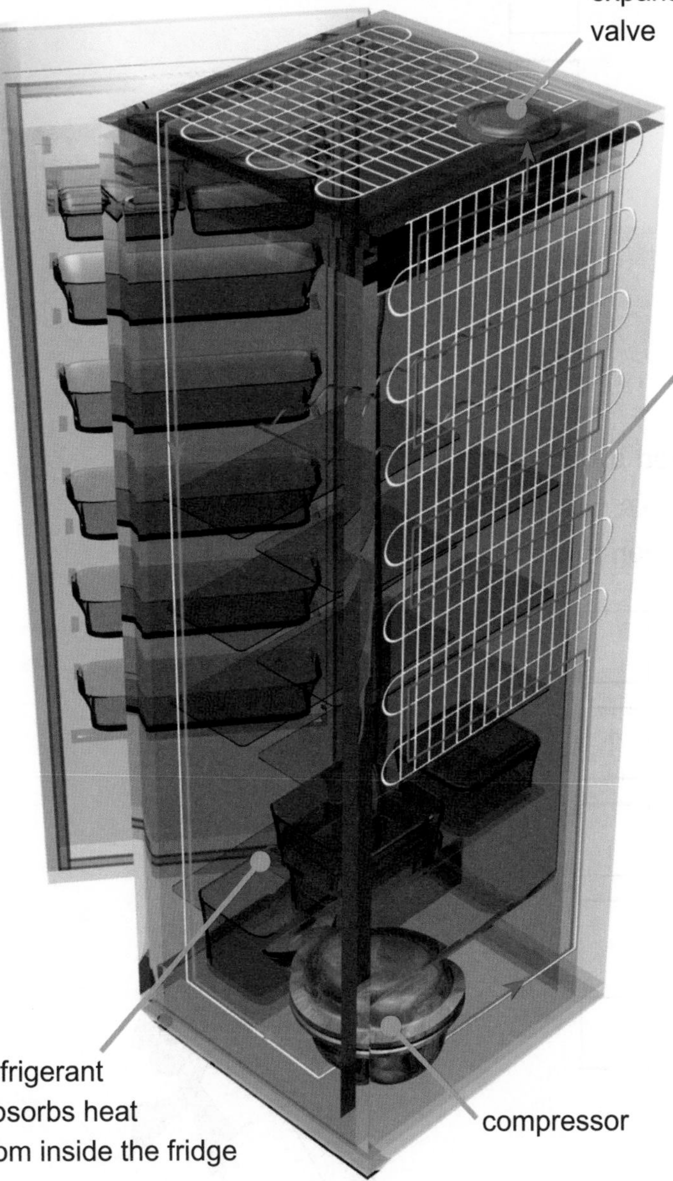

5. STAYING AT THE RIGHT TEMPERATURE

The compressor is controlled by a **thermostat** — a device that regulates temperature. The compressor starts pumping when the fridge's temperature starts to rise, and stops when the fridge cools to the desired degree.

An adapted extract from *Stuff You Should Know!* by John Farndon and Rob Beattie.

Consider

What's important to include in an explanation text?
Is the layout important? What type of vocabulary should be used?

Refrigerators — Question Set 1

1 **This is an explanation text. What would be a better title than 'Refrigerators'?** 2C

....

2 **Why is a fridge so important?** 2B

Tick one box

because food tastes better cold ☐

because you can store all your food in it ☐

because it stops food from going off ☐

because it freezes all your food ☐

3 **The refrigerant is the special fluid pumped around the fridge. Number these places the refrigerant travels so that they are in the correct order. The first one has been done for you.** 2C

into the compressor ☐

into the fridge 1

across the back of the fridge ☐

down to the bottom of the fridge ☐

into a series of pipes ☐

4 **Find a word in the text that means the refrigerant is pumped 'all the time' around the fridge.** 2A

....

Search the text for the part where it is describing the refrigerant being pumped around.

5 **The text is written in sections, some of which are numbered. Match each subheading to what its section is about.** 2C

KEEPING COOL	Pressure applied to the refrigerant turns it back into liquid form.
INTO THE INTERIOR	The thermostat makes sure the fridge is not too hot or too cold.
BACK TO THE COMPRESSOR	Heat is released into the air.
HEAT LOSS	The pipes in the fridge carry the refrigerant around.
STAYING AT THE RIGHT TEMPERATURE	Water evaporates into vapour.

6 **a) In the text, some words are written in bold. Why do you think is?** 2F

....

....

b) Match the words written in bold from the text, with their meaning. 2A

vapour	a small pump
evaporate	a narrow, funnel-shaped tube
nozzle	a device for controlling temperature
thermostat	turn from liquid into vapour
compressor	tiny drops of liquid suspended in the air

Do the ones you know first and make sure you refer back to the text to make sure your answers make sense.

Refrigerators — Question Set 2

(1) **Why is a cool fridge *BAD NEWS FOR GERMS*?** 2G

....

....

(2) **The first two paragraphs and the paragraph entitled *BAD NEWS FOR GERMS* are not numbered like the other paragraphs. Why is this?** 2H

....

....

....

(3) **Tick to show if the following statements are true or false.** 2D

	True	**False**
Food stays fresh forever in a fridge.	☐	☐
To stay warm after a swim, you should dry off.	☐	☐
The refrigerant absorbs heat from within the fridge.	☐	☐
When it gets too cold inside the fridge, the compressor starts pumping.	☐	☐

You'll need to find evidence in the text to help you decide whether each statement is true or false.

4 **Find and copy two words or phrases from section 5 that show the temperature of the fridge is managed.**

2A

1. ....

....

2. ....

....

5 **Why do you think this explanation text has a diagram of a fridge as well as writing?**

2F

....

....

....

....

Challenge

I think I understand how the fridge works: the refrigerant kills the germs which keeps the food fresh.

Can you explain to the giraffe why he's wrong? Justify your explanation by describing what the refrigerant actually does.

....

....

....

....

....

2C

Welcome Home, Anna Hibiscus!

This text is taken from a story about a girl called Anna Hibiscus who lives in Africa with her cousin Chocolate and her friend Benz. Anna is looking after a newborn chick who she has named Snow White. In this part of the story, Anna decides to take Snow White with her to school.

The next day Anna Hibiscus did not leave Snow White in the house. But she did not leave Snow White in the compound either. She put Snow White in her lunch box and took Snow White to school.

Anna Hibiscus sang loudly along with the radio all the way so that nobody would hear the *"Cheep! Cheep!"* coming from the lunch box on her lap.

At school, Anna Hibiscus opened her lunch box and put it inside the desk. Then she quickly closed the desk so that Snow White could not jump out.

When the teacher came in, all the children stopped talking and stood up quietly.

"Let us sing our national anthem!" said the teacher.

"Cheep! Cheep!" said Anna Hibiscus's desk.

Chocolate looked at Anna. Benz looked at Anna. The teacher looked at Anna. Anna Hibiscus started to sing loudly and the teacher and all the children joined in.

"Well done, Anna Hibiscus," said the teacher. "You sang well today."

"Cheep!" said Anna Hibiscus's desk.

The teacher looked surprised.

"Thank you!" said Anna Hibiscus loudly.

"You can sit down now," said the teacher. "Let me hear the times tables."

So Anna Hibiscus and all the other children in the class said the times tables. They started well with the two times table. But by the time they arrived at the eight times table, they were struggling.

"You started well," said the teacher. "But you ended poorly. Let me hear the eight times table again."

"Cheep! Cheep!" said Anna's desk loudly.

Chocolate and Benz looked at each other with wide eyes.

"What was that?" asked the teacher.

"Eight times one is eight," said Anna loudly. "Eight times two is sixteen."

"Good," said the teacher. "Continue, Anna."

"Cheep! Cheep!"

"Eight times three is twenty-four."

Anna Hibiscus stopped. She did not know any more.
She had been so busy with Snow White's trouble that she had forgotten to practise.

"I said continue," said the teacher.

"Cheep! Cheep!" said Anna Hibiscus's desk.

"What?" asked the teacher crossly.

Chocolate put up her hand.

"Eight times four is thirty-two. Eight times five is forty. Eight times six is forty-eight. Eight times seven is fifty-six. Eight times eight is sixty-four. Eight times nine is seventy-two. Eight times ten is eighty," she said loudly. Chocolate loved maths.

"Very good," said the teacher.

"Cheep! Cheep!" said Anna Hibiscus's desk.

"Who is making that noise?" asked the teacher crossly.

The whole class looked at Anna Hibiscus.

"DING-A-LING!" rang the school bell. It was time for break.

As soon as the teacher had gone, Chocolate and Benz came to Anna's desk.

"Anna Hibiscus," said Benz, "what is that noise coming from your desk?"

"Did you bring Snow White to school?" asked Chocolate.

Anna Hibiscus crossed her fingers and shook her head.

An extract from *Welcome Home, Anna Hibiscus!* by Atinuke.

Consider

What do you think might happen after play time? Do you think the teacher will eventually find out about the chick in the classroom?

Welcome Home, Anna Hibiscus! — Question Set 1

1. **How did Anna get the baby chick to school without it being noticed?** 2B

....

....

2. **How do the class show respect to their teacher when she enters the classroom?** 2D

Tick one box

They start singing the national anthem.	☐
They recite their times tables.	☐
They stop talking and stand up.	☐
They say good morning.	☐

You're not just looking for something the class does, but for something that shows respect to a teacher.

3. **Why does the teacher want the class to do the eight times table again?** 2B

....

....

Scan the text for the words 'eight times table' and then read around that part of the text.

4 **Draw lines to match each character with the most appropriate description for them.** 2B

Anna Hibiscus	loves maths
Chocolate	becomes cross in the text
the teacher	has forgotten to learn the eight times table
Benz	is Anna's friend

Do the ones you're most sure of first — then try to do the ones you're less sure of.

5 **Why has the author described Benz and Chocolate as looking at each other with *wide eyes*?** 2G

....

....

....

Describing facial expressions is a good way to show how characters are feeling. How are Chocolate and Benz feeling at this point in the story?

6 **List three things that stop Anna from having to explain to the teacher what the *Cheep! Cheep!* noise is.** 2B

1. ....

....

2. ....

....

3. ....

....

Welcome Home, Anna Hibiscus! — Question Set 2

1. a) **Why do you think Anna decides not to leave Snow White at home?** 2D

....

....

b) **What evidence can you find to support your answer?** 2A

....

....

2. **Why does Chocolate finish the eight times table when Anna struggles?** 2D

Tick one box

because she loves maths ☐

because she wants to help Anna cover up the noise of the chick ☐

because the teacher asks her to ☐

because it's her turn ☐

Here you have to dig beneath the surface of the text to <u>infer</u> what the character's motives are.

3. **Which two words in the text show that the class didn't do the eight times table very well the first time?** 2A

1. ....

2. ....

The question asks for <u>two</u> words <u>from the text</u>. Don't write anything else!

4 **Why do you think Anna has lied to Chocolate and Benz about bringing Snow White to school?**

2D

....

....

5 **Number these events in the order they happen in the extract. One has been done for you.**

2C

Anna lies about Snow White.	☐
Anna sings the national anthem.	☐
Anna begins the eight times table on her own.	☐
Anna sings along with the radio.	1
Anna puts Snow White into her desk.	☐

Remember — <u>find</u> and <u>underline</u> the events in the text. <u>Number</u> them in the text, then <u>match</u> the events in the question to these numbers.

Challenge

How lovely – it must be 'bring your pet to school day' at Anna Hibiscus's school!

Explain the mistake that the cow has made in reading the extract. Support your explanation with evidence from the text.

....

....

....

....

2D

Say No to Bullying

Remember to read the introduction. It might contain important information.

Sometimes writers can try to persuade you to agree with their point of view or even get you to change your behaviour. The following extract is taken from the non-fiction book *Say No To Bullying*. Here, the writer tries to persuade any readers who are being bullied that they can do something about it.

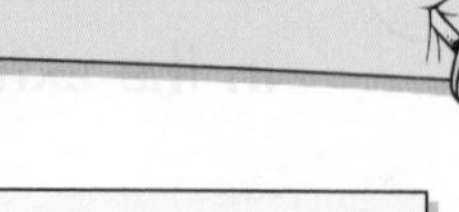

Say No to Bullying

One of the things that makes it so hard to say no to bullying is that targets of bullying often feel alone. They might think that they are the only ones being bullied or that no one else understands how they feel or gets what it is like to be them.

You're not alone

Some people think there's no choice but to accept the things that are happening to them and that they just have to learn to put up with it. Not so! Bullying is not something we can or should ignore and it's absolutely critical to remember you are not alone if you are being bullied. Nearly everyone is, has been or will be bullied at some time in their lives by people at school, by brothers and sisters, or by adults. There are many other people like you that face bullying every day.

Did you know?

A recent study has found that about one quarter of all schoolchildren in the UK are bullied at some point in their school lives and another study found that fear of bullying was a serious issue for more than half of them.

Taking the first steps

If you're being bullied it can be hard to believe that you can do anything about it. After all, you don't have much of a choice about where you live, go to school, or even go out to play football or meet friends. And because bullies push you around you probably feel utterly powerless too. But you can do something about bullying and you're already taking the first steps by reading this book. You can learn and practise things to do in different situations and how to get other people involved when you need to. You can try to change things and you can sort out the situation so that the bullying stops.

YOU CAN DO IT!

You can turn things around — just look at all the other people who've been bullied but made good. Famous footballer David Beckham was bullied: 'There was a bullying side to starting sport so young. Because you're not going out, on the Monday at school, people would be like, 'You stayed in, you played football.' But I bumped into those same people and they were like, 'Can we come and watch you play?'

An extract from *Say No to Bullying* by Louise Spilsbury.

Discuss

What do you think are the five most important things to remember or do if you are being bullied? Discuss your ideas with a partner. Do you agree with each other? Do you have different ideas?

Say No to Bullying — Question Set 1

1 **Who is this text aimed at?** 2C

....

2 **a) Read the statements below carefully.
Put a tick next to the statements that are true.** 2B

Many people will experience some kind of bullying in their lives. ☐

About half of all children will be bullied at some point whilst at school. ☐

Fear of bullying is a serious issue for many children. ☐

The text encourages readers to believe they can do something about bullying. ☐

b) Rewrite any false statements so they are true. 2B

....

....

3 **Who is the famous footballer who was bullied as a child?** 2B

....

Who?
What?
Where?
When?
Why?

When a question begins with 'who', you are looking for a person.

4 In the paragraph below the subheading *You're not alone*, find two examples where the writing is aimed directly at the reader. 2F

1. ....

....

2. ....

....

Direct address is when the writer seems to be speaking to you as the reader personally.

5 Why do you think the subheading *YOU CAN DO IT!* is written in capital letters? 2F

....

....

Think about why you might sometimes write something in capital letters, and what effect you hope it will have on the reader.

6 Which of the following phrases is most similar in meaning to the words *absolutely critical* found in the second paragraph of the text? 2A

Tick one box

really awful	☐
incredibly easy	☐
quite difficult	☐
very important	☐

Try replacing the words with the different options to find out which one fits best in the sentence.

Dictionary

Say No to Bullying — Question Set 2

(1) *Say No to Bullying* is a persuasive text.
Which of the following features are used?

2F

Tick all that apply

use of facts and figures from research ☐

rhetorical question ☐

quote ☐

character development ☐

The question says 'which of the following features are used' so you'll need to tick more than one box.

(2) Look at the paragraph under the subheading *You're not alone*.
Which phrase shows that the author is determined to make the person who is being bullied see that they can do something about it?

2G

....

Remember, a phrase is a group of words. Which phrase does the author use to make an impact on the reader?

(3) Why do you think the author decided to mention the recent study?

2D

....

....

....

....

4. **Draw lines to match each subheading with a summary of its paragraph.** 2C

You're not alone	an example of how things can get better
Did you know?	ideas for what you can begin to do to make things better
Taking the first steps	advice to make you realise that bullying happens to many people
YOU CAN DO IT!	facts and figures based on bullying research

5. **Which of the paragraphs do you think will have the most positive effect on someone who is being bullied? Explain why you have chosen this paragraph.** 2H

....

....

....

....

It doesn't matter which paragraph you choose as long as you can explain why you have chosen it.

Challenge

Find three pieces of evidence from the text that suggest bullying is a widespread problem.

1. ....

....

2. ....

....

3. ....

....

2F

The Suitcase Kid

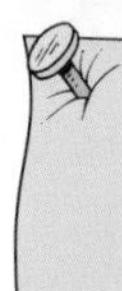

Stories often explore difficult issues such as changes in families. The following extract is taken from the novel *The Suitcase Kid* by Jacqueline Wilson. It's about a ten-year-old girl called Andy whose parents are getting divorced.

When my parents split up they didn't know what to do with me. My mum wanted me to go and live with her. My dad wanted me to go and live with him. I didn't want to go and live at my mum's new place or my dad's new place. I wanted to stay living in our *old* place, Mulberry Cottage, the three of us together. Four, counting my pet Sylvanian family spotted rabbit Radish.

There were all these arguments about who would get custody of me. I thought they were talking about custard at first. I hate custard because you can never tell when there's going to be a lump and it sticks in your throat and makes you shudder.

My mum got mad and my dad got mad and I got mad too. I felt *I* was being split up. Half of me wanted to side with Mum. Half of me wanted to side with Dad. It was much easier for Radish. She just sided with me. She lives in my pocket so there's never been any hassle over who gets custody of her.

We had to go for family counselling. It seemed a bit daft because my mum and dad didn't want to be a family anymore. This lady chatted to me. She was trying to be ever so casual but I knew she was trying to suss things out. She had some little dolls in her office, a mummy doll and a daddy doll and a whole set of children dolls in different sizes. She wanted me to play with them. I poked the mummy doll and the daddy doll in the stomachs and said I didn't like playing with silly old dolls.

But this lady saw me fiddling around in my pocket and she got a glimpse of Radish. I like to hold her tight when I'm feeling funny.

"Oh, what a dear little toy. Do let me have a look," she said, in that silly voice grown-ups always use when they're trying to get you to like them.

"She's not a toy, she's a mascot," I said. I didn't want to show her Radish at all. She's mine and she's private. But I had to let this lady paw at her and undo her frock and turn her upside down, in a very rude sort of way.

"What's Bunny's name?" she asked.

You'd have thought I was two years old, not ten. I just shrugged and shook my head.

An extract from *The Suitcase Kid* by Jacqueline Wilson.

Discuss

Why do you think the counsellor tries to talk to Andy about Radish? Discuss your thoughts with a partner.

The Suitcase Kid — Question Set 1

(1) **Where did Andy want to live?** 2B

....

When a question begins with 'where', you need to give a place for the answer.

Who? What? Where? When? Why?

(2) **a)** ***There were all these arguments about who would get custody of me.*** **Think about the meaning of the word *custody*. Which of the following sentences does not use the word *custody* correctly?** 2A

Tick one box

The judge gave custody to the grandparents.	☐
Her husband had custody of their son.	☐
The teacher gave a custody to the child for bad behaviour.	☐

b) Why do you think Andy thought they were talking about custard? 2D

....

(3) **'I felt *I* was being split up.'**
Why has the writer written the second 'I' in italics? 2F

....

Read the sentence out loud.
What do the italics make you do?
What is the effect of this?

4 **Use the text to help match the first half of the sentence (on the left) with the correct ending (on the right).**

2B

Andy's mum and dad both wanted her to	play with the dolls.
The counsellor wanted Andy to	share the name of her mascot.
Andy wanted to	live in their new houses.
Andy did not want to	keep Radish in her pocket.

5 **Give three reasons why Andy did not enjoy the family counselling.**

2D

1. ....

....

2. ....

....

3. ....

....

6 **Find and copy one sentence from the text which shows how important Radish is to Andy.**

2G

....

The Suitcase Kid — Question Set 2

1 **Why do you think Andy wanted to live in her old house?** 2D

....

....

2 **Write down two occasions in the text when Andy is cross.** 2F

1. ....

....

2. ....

....

Look for where in the text it says that Andy got cross. Also, look for things that Andy says or does that show she is cross.

3 **What does Andy think about the counsellor?**
What evidence is there to support your answer? 2C

Andy thinks:	....
Evidence from the text:	....

Read from *We had to go for family counselling* to the end of the text before answering this question.

4 **Why do you think Andy doesn't want to talk about Radish with the counsellor?** 2D

....

....

5 **What information do you think the counsellor finds out about Andy's feelings during the session? Find and copy evidence to support your answer.** 2D

The counsellor might think:	....
Evidence from the text:	....

This is a tricky question. Think about what Andy does or says and how that might show her feelings.

Challenge

A mascot is a person or thing that brings you good luck. Why do you think Andy says about Radish, "She's not a toy, she's a mascot"?

....

....

....

....

2F

The Search for Odysseus

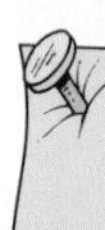

In Greek mythology, the hero Odysseus fought and blinded the Cyclops, a giant with one eye who was called Polyphemus. The following extract is taken from the play *The Search for Odysseus*, which tells how Odysseus's son, Telemachus, goes in search of his father. Here, Telemachus and Athene visit the island of the Cyclops.

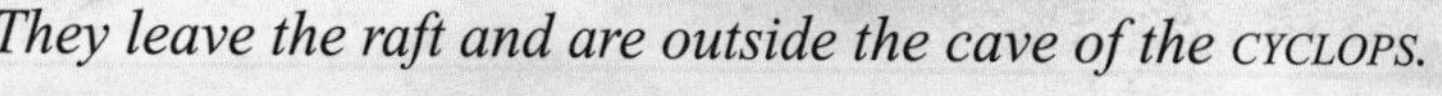

They leave the raft and are outside the cave of the CYCLOPS.
We hear the sound of hammer on anvil. It gets louder then stops.

TELEMACHUS What sounds are these?

ATHENE Where are you going? (*pulls him back*)

TELEMACHUS Are you afraid?

ATHENE Of course I'm afraid. He eats people.

TELEMACHUS What happened to your curiosity? Your love of adventure?

ATHENE Perhaps we should hide, survey the creature from a distance.

TELEMACHUS If I hide, I'll have time to think. If I have time to think I'll be overcome with dread. Come let's speak with him and be gone.

ATHENE Wait! Wait! Why this sudden impetuousness. Speak with him by all means, but try not to be so…

TELEMACHUS So?

ATHENE Honest. Don't be so ready to tell him who you really are — it gets us into trouble.

TELEMACHUS I'm not a good liar.

ATHENE Poor liars make good meals.

Lights now reveal the back of the cave and we see the giant as a huge blacksmith. His one eye is now sightless. He fumbles round his cave for his tools. He curses under his breath. He then stops and smells the scent of TELEMACHUS.

CYCLOPS Who's there? I will find you wherever you are. I can smell the sweat on your skin, the sea in your hair, the food on your breath. Speak to me. (*He picks up one of his blacksmiths' tools which becomes a weapon.*) Who's there?

TELEMACHUS A friend.

CYCLOPS I have no friends. What friends I had — I had for dinner. (*He takes a lunge for TELEMACHUS who leaps aside.*)

TELEMACHUS I mean you no harm Cyclops.

CYCLOPS (*throws back his head and laughs a huge resounding laugh*) What harm can you do me? Your throat is no wider than a reed pipe, your voice no deeper than a song bird.

TELEMACHUS turns to ATHENE and she shakes her head and puts her finger to her lips.

TELEMACHUS (*mouths*) He's blind.

CYCLOPS Are you alone — little one? (*silence*) Since I lost my sight my sense of smell has increased tenfold — but yet though I sense another, I smell only one.

TELEMACHUS I'm not alone. I have a whole crew of sailors waiting on the beach, who will come and slay you if I don't return by nightfall.

CYCLOPS Poor little songbird, you cannot even lie with conviction. (*He makes another grab for TELEMACHUS. TELEMACHUS drops his sword — the giant picks it up.*) What do you want of Polyphemus? Have you come to kill me? Tell me the truth.

TELEMACHUS I'm looking for someone.

CYCLOPS You are fortunate to have eyes — I am not so lucky. (*He makes another grab for TELEMACHUS who again avoids him.*) Whom do you seek?

TELEMACHUS Odysseus. The Hero of Troy.

CYCLOPS Odysseus. What is he — to you?

TELEMACHUS My — my enemy.

An extract from *The Search for Odysseus* by Charles Way.

Consider

Imagine seeing this playscript acted out. Find three things in the text which would make it dramatic when acted out. Remember to consider the stage directions as well as the dialogue.

The Search for Odysseus — Question Set 1

1 **The layout of this extract shows it's a playscript. Which of these features does it have?** 2B

Tick all that apply

a short description to set the scene ☐

character names to show who's speaking ☐

indication of act and scene number ☐

character directions within speech ☐

stage directions between speech ☐

2 **Read the conversation between Athene and Telemachus up until *Poor liars make good meals*. What is Athene trying to do in her advice to Telemachus?** 2C

....

....

....

In this question you have to get in the mind of one of the characters and work out what is motivating them.

3 **The Cyclops has been blinded in his fight with Odysseus, so how does the Cyclops know that he is not alone in the cave?** 2B

Tick one box

Telemachus drops something on the floor of the cave. ☐

He hears Athene and Telemachus approaching. ☐

He smells the sweat of Telemachus. ☐

Telemachus's voice is so deep he hears it. ☐

4 **Draw lines to match the words found in the playscript (on the left) with their correct meanings (on the right).** 2A

impetuousness	confidence
tenfold	observe
survey	acting without thought or care
conviction	kill
slay	ten times as big

When you have to match words with their meanings, it helps to replace that word in the text with the meaning to see if it makes sense.

5 **Number the following events in the order they happen. One has been done for you.** 2C

The Cyclops senses that someone is with him in the cave. [3]

Telemachus lies about his father. [ ]

Athene tries to warn Telemachus about the dangers ahead. [ ]

Odysseus blinds the Cyclops during a fight. [ ]

The Cyclops laughs at the thought that Telemachus might harm him. [ ]

You need to be careful and methodical with questions like this. Remember to check your answer when you think you've got the right order.

6 **In your own words, explain why Telemachus does not want to hide from the Cyclops.** 2B

....

....

....

The Search for Odysseus — Question Set 2

1 **What do each of these quotes suggest that the Cyclops thinks of Telemachus? Draw lines to match the quote with its meaning.** 2G

Quote	Meaning
'Your throat is no wider than a reed pipe'	You are more like a boy than a man.
'your voice no deeper than a song bird.'	You do not convince me of your bravery.
'you cannot even lie with conviction.'	You are so small in comparison to me.

2 **Find and copy two pieces of evidence from the text which show how dangerous the Cyclops is.** 2D

1. ....

....

2. ....

....

Remember — when a question asks for evidence, you have to copy carefully from the text.

3 **At the beginning of the extract, Telemachus wants Athene to have more curiosity and love for adventure. Do you think Telemachus still feels this by the end of the extract? Support your answer with reasoning.** 2H

....

....

....

....

4 At the end of this extract, Telemachus hesitates when he is asked about Odysseus: *My — my enemy.* Why do you think Telemachus hesitates at this point?

2D

....

....

This is an inference question. You have to work out what's going on under the surface of the text.

5 What evidence is there in the text that this is not the first time Athene and Telemachus have been in a dangerous or troublesome situation?

2D

....

....

....

....

Challenge

Telemachus is right to lie about his relationship with Odysseus.

Do you agree or disagree? Why? Give reasons and evidence from the text to support your thinking.

....

....

....

....

....

2D

Answers

Text 1 — Historical Story

Pages 6 and 7: Black Beauty — Question Set 1

1. You should have matched these phrases:
   Black Beauty — the horse
   Anna Sewell — the author
   John — the horse's groom
2. The oak tree (that fell across the road)
3. Black Beauty was frightened by the tree falling. — true
   Squire Gordon stood by Black Beauty to comfort him. — false
   They decided to continue on their journey by travelling around the oak tree. — false
   Black Beauty knew something was wrong before he stepped on the bridge. — false
   The man waving a torch at them and shouting was on the other side of the bridge. — true
4. Squire Gordon used his whip (first a light touch and then a sharper hit).
   John (gets out of the cart and) tries to lead him.
5. Where it is broken, part of the bridge has been washed away by the river.
6. You should have given the events the following numbers:
   They turn around and go back the way they came. — 3
   They are informed of the broken bridge. — 5
   Sensing danger, Black Beauty refuses to cross the bridge. — 4
   A large oak tree crashes to the ground in front of them. — 2

Pages 8 and 9: Black Beauty — Question Set 2

1. You should have circled:
   I had not been trained to do that.
2. a) To show how determined the horse was in not going any further OR to show how still the horse was when he stopped and that he would be really difficult to move.
   b) You should have copied the phrase:
   'I dare not stir' OR 'I dared not go forward'
3. The groom speaks to the horse, asking 'What's the matter?' He also tells the master 'there's something wrong' because of the horse's reaction to crossing the bridge. This shows he understands the horse is scared of something.
4. In the future, John will listen and watch out for Black Beauty's reactions and responses, particularly in potentially dangerous situations. He could save their lives again.
5. You should have ticked this statement:
   John felt immensely proud of Black Beauty for saving them.

Challenge:
Example:
What: I think Black Beauty deserves the medal.
Why: He refuses to cross the bridge in spite of being whipped.
Evidence: 'He gave me a sharp cut; I jumped, but I dared not go forward'
OR
What: I think John deserves the medal.
Why: He decides to trust Black Beauty.
Evidence: He tells Squire Gordon 'There's something wrong, sir'

Text 2 — Newspaper Article

Pages 12 and 13: Pheasant's Revolt — Question Set 1

1. The pheasant has been hurting the residents. — true
   The residents have been feeding the pheasant. — false
   The pheasant has jumped on to cars in the street. — true
   The pheasant leaves the postmen alone. — false
   Umbrellas are being used as defensive weapons. — true
2. You should have circled: alliteration
3. a) squirt vinegar at him, use high-pitched sensors, use gun noises
   b) Example:
   I think squirting Phil with vinegar is the best because the article says high pitched sensors and gun noises 'failed to work'.
4. You should have matched these phrases:
   like a velociraptor — Sonya Bolton
   lethal — a postman
   aggressive — the university lecturer
   trying to establish a pecking order — the RSPB
5. You should have ticked: delighting
6. Example:

My advice:	Carry an umbrella with you to protect yourself
Evidence from the text:	'Resident Shahin Assadinia, 39, now carries an umbrella to protect himself from the pesky pheasant.'

Pages 14 and 15: Pheasant's Revolt — Question Set 2

1. You should have picked out two of the following phrases:
   'forces residents to stay in their homes'
   'She can only leave the house with me so I can shield her.'
   'We're all scared' (allow this even though this is the reaction of the postmen)
   'now carries an umbrella to protect himself'
   'He's really getting on my nerves'

Answers

2. The answer should draw comparisons between the two animals. Example:
   I think Sonya compares Phil to a velociraptor because they are both quick moving and dangerous creatures and it feels impossible to get away from them like when she explains that he had pinned the postie up against their door. Velociraptors have sharp claws like the pheasant who has given nasty scratches to his victims.
3. Example:
   He means that the pheasant thinks the street where the residents live is actually his own home and so he should be in charge — it's right next to the woods where the pheasant's real home probably is.
4. Example:

Action needed:	Reason why they should intervene:
1. Witness the pheasant's attacks.	They should see how scared residents are of him — they might decide to hurt him soon.
2. Capture and take away the pheasant.	He is in danger from people who are defending themselves with umbrellas.

5. Any three of the following examples:
   pounces on residents, chews/pecks at wipers on a car, scratches a postman, pins a postman up against a door, pecks at people's feet, bites residents, chases residents, claws residents, chases residents' pets, jumps on cars

Challenge:
Your answer can either agree or disagree as long as you've given reasoning to support your ideas.
Example:
I don't agree because the pheasant has been causing havoc! He has been stopping the postmen from being able to do their job properly; he's been hurting people by scratching them and pecking at them; and he's been damaging property too. The people are right not to befriend him and should be doing everything they can to get rid of him.

Text 3 — Fantasy Fiction

Pages 18 and 19: Gregor and the Curse of the Warmbloods — Question Set 1

1. Any two of the following: the campfire is out, his flashlight is off, the lanterns were not lit
2. They are larger and more explosive than the ones he had seen before.
3. You should have matched these pairs:
   emanate — spread out
   dissolved — disappeared
   tainted — polluted
   bait — food
4. 'hundreds of those streams crisscrossing the jungle'
5. You should have given the events the following numbers:
   Ripred warns Gregor of the dangers of the stream. — 2
   Boots remembers being hurt by hot water before. — 5
   Gregor is confused about where the light is coming from. — 1
   Boots becomes upset at the way Gregor speaks. — 4
6. Examples:
   To show he is exclaiming these words and to match the sharp tone he speaks in. OR To show he might be shouting the words at Boots. OR To show how important what he is saying is.

Pages 20 and 21: Gregor and the Curse of the Warmbloods — Question Set 2

1. Ripred warns him of the dangers.
   A set of spiky teeth snap together in the water.
2. a) You could have circled any of the characters for your answer provided that you have offered a sensible reason in part b).
   b) Examples:
   (*Ripred*) Ripred seems the most knowledgeable about the jungle and so he would be able to keep them safe.
   (*Gregor*) Temp and Boots seem to listen to Gregor and take orders from him.
3. Examples:
   she hasn't understood Gregor OR she only hears the word 'water'
4. You should have ticked: Boots becomes upset.
5. 'Ow'

Challenge
You should have circled 'I would not have drunk from the stream'.
You could have mentioned one of the following:
Reason: The water might cause me harm.
Evidence: Ripred says '... the water's tainted. Drink it and you die.'
OR
Reason: The water is warm so it wouldn't have cooled me down.
Evidence: 'Gregor dipped his fingers in the stream and felt the warm water roll over them.'

Answers

Text 4 — Non-Chronological Report

Pages 24 and 25: The Brilliance of Bees — Question Set 1

1. You should have ticked: visit two million flowers, fly 88,000 km
2. You should have circled: liquid
3. You should have given the statements the following numbers:
   The nectar becomes honey and is stored in the honeycomb. — 4
   The female honey bee returns to the hive. — 2
   A layer of beeswax is used to seal the honeycomb. — 5
   The honey-making bees chew the nectar to make it dry. — 3
4. delicious
5. You should have ticked: large group of animals living together
6. You should have matched these pairs:
   Long grass helps — to give bees shelter.
   Pollen is moved when — bees fly from flower to flower.
   Bee bread is made when — nectar and water are mixed with pollen grains.
   A layer of beeswax is used — to help keep the honey fresh.

Pages 26 and 27: The Brilliance of Bees — Question Set 2

1. Examples:
   (*The bee can carry*) It is comparing how much a bee can carry with how much a person can carry.
   (*If the honey*) It is explaining what the bees do if the honey is not dry enough.
2. Because it is where a female bee keeps the nectar that she collects. The bee has another normal stomach.
3. Examples:
   (*Yes*) It is a good idea because the bee can tell all the other bees where to find the honey without having to move from that place. OR It is a good idea because the other bees know where to go and how far away it is.
   (*No*) It is not a good idea because if there are too many bees that come, there might not be enough nectar for them all.
4. Any one of the following points:
   - use of the word 'special'
   - use of the word 'perfect'
   - use of the expression 'bee bread'
   - use of an exclamation mark after 'bee bread'
5. a) 'Honey bees need our help' OR The part that starts 'Bees are in trouble' OR The last section of the writing.
   b) subheadings

Challenge:
Your answer should include reference to:
- pollination
- the need for fruit and plants
- humans needing food

Your answer may also refer to:
- delicious honey to eat

Text 5 — Explanation Text

Pages 30 and 31: Refrigerators — Question Set 1

1. How a refrigerator works
   It's not correct to say refrigerator OR about a refrigerator.
2. You should have ticked this statement:
   because it stops food from going off
3. You should have given the places the following numbers:
   into the compressor — 4
   across the back of the fridge — 5
   down to the bottom of the fridge — 3
   into a series of pipes — 2
4. continuously
5. You should have matched these pairs:
   INTO THE INTERIOR — The pipes in the fridge carry the refrigerant around.
   BACK TO THE COMPRESSOR — Pressure applied to the refrigerant turns it back into liquid form.
   HEAT LOSS — Heat is released into the air.
   STAYING AT THE RIGHT TEMPERATURE — The thermostat makes sure the fridge is not too hot or too cold.
6. a) To show that they are important.
   They are technical words and it's important to know what they mean to be able to understand the text.
   b) You should have matched these pairs:
   vapour — tiny drops of liquid suspended in the air
   evaporate — turn from liquid into vapour
   nozzle — a narrow, funnel-shaped tube
   thermostat — a device for controlling temperature
   compressor — a small pump

Pages 32 and 33: Refrigerators — Question Set 2

1. Example:
   Germs grow well in warm conditions, so the refrigerator is the bad news because it is cold so the germs can't grow so quickly.
2. Example:
   They are not numbered because they are not part of the explanation which describes the journey of the refrigerant and the order in which it moves.
3. Food stays fresh forever in a fridge. — false
   To stay warm after a swim, you should dry off. — true
   The refrigerant absorbs heat from within the fridge. — true
   When it gets too cold inside the fridge, the compressor starts pumping. — false

Answers

4. Any two of the following phrases: 'staying at the right temperature', 'regulates temperature', 'starts pumping when the refrigerator's temperature starts to rise', 'cools to the desired degree'.
5. Example: The diagram shows the reader the parts of the fridge that the author is talking about. Without the diagram, it would be difficult to understand the journey of the refrigerant and also most people haven't seen the back of the fridge before.

Challenge

Example: The refrigerant doesn't kill the germs, but it's still important because it keeps the fridge cold. This means that the germs can't grow quickly. It travels all around the fridge through pipes taking heat away from the food.
You might also have mentioned the important job of the thermostat which controls how cold the fridge gets.

Text 6 — Children's Fiction

Pages 36 and 37: Welcome Home, Anna Hibiscus! — Question Set 1

1. She hid it in her lunch box. She also sang loudly to cover the 'Cheep! Cheep!' sounds.
2. You should have ticked:
   They stop talking and stand up.
3. Because they struggled with it the first time
4. You should have matched these pairs:
   Anna Hibiscus — has forgotten to learn the eight times tables
   Chocolate — loves maths
   the teacher — becomes cross in this extract
   Benz — is Anna's friend
5. Examples:
   To show how astonished/surprised they are.
   They had realised that Snow White was in Anna's desk.
6. Any three of the following:
   Anna starts singing the national anthem loudly, Anna starts reciting her times tables, Chocolate continues to recite the eight times tables, the play time bell rings

Pages 38 and 39: Welcome Home, Anna Hibiscus! — Question Set 2

1. a) She thinks the chick needs looking after.
   b) The introduction says it's a 'newborn chick'. OR The text says 'She had been so busy with Snow White's trouble'.
   It's not correct to say Anna was showing off the chick to her friends because the text only mentions Anna hiding the chick and lying about having it at school.
2. You should have ticked this statement:
   because she wants to help Anna cover up the noise of the chick
3. struggling, poorly
4. Anna is worried that they might tell the teacher and then she will get into trouble.
   OR
   Anna knows what she has done is wrong and she doesn't want to get Benz and Chocolate into trouble.
5. You should have given the events the following numbers:
   Anna lies about Snow White. — 5
   Anna sings the national anthem. — 3
   Anna begins the eight times table on her own. — 4
   Anna puts Snow White into her desk. — 2

Challenge

Any relevant answer that explains why it is not 'bring your pet to school day'.
It isn't 'bring your pet to school' day because:
Examples:
• Anna spends the whole time in this extract trying to hide Snow White and the cheep noises the chick keeps making.
• She also doesn't tell the teacher that the chick is there and at the end of the text she even lies to her friend and cousin.
• If it was 'bring your pet to school' day, other children would have brought their pets in and the teacher would have spoken to the class about it.

Text 7 — Persuasive Text

Pages 42 and 43: Say No to Bullying — Question Set 1

1. People who are being bullied or people who know someone who's being bullied
2. a) You should have ticked these statements:
   Many people will experience some kind of bullying in their lives.
   Fear of bullying is a serious issue for many children.
   The text encourages readers to believe they can do something about bullying.
   b) You should have rewritten the second statement:
   About one quarter of all school children in the UK are bullied at some point in their school lives.
3. David Beckham
4. Any two of the following examples:
   'Bullying is not something we can or should ignore'
   'you are not alone if you are being bullied'
   'people like you that face bullying every day'
5. It is written in capital letters to emphasise how important the message is and to draw attention to it.
6. You should have ticked: very important

Pages 44 and 45: Say No to Bullying — Question Set 2

1. You should have ticked these features:
   use of facts and figures from research
   rhetorical question
   quote
2. Not so!

Answers

3. Any of the following points:
   - to tell people about research which has been done
   - to show what a serious issue it is with so many children affected
   - to show the author's views are backed up by other evidence
4. You're not alone — advice to make you realise that bullying happens to many people
   Did you know? — facts and figures based on bullying research
   Taking the first steps — ideas for what you can begin to do to make things better
   YOU CAN DO IT! — an example of how things can get better
5. Any suitable response and explanation. Example:
   I think 'You're not alone' will have the most positive impact because it will make people feel like they're not the only one going through a bad time and that maybe if they talk about it they might find that someone else they know has had the same experience.

Challenge

Examples:
'Nearly everyone is, has been or will be bullied'
'There are many other people like you that face bullying every day'
'one quarter of all schoolchildren in the UK are bullied at some point'
Even successful people like David Beckham have experienced bullying.

Text 8 — Children's Fiction

Pages 48 and 49: The Suitcase Kid — Question Set 1

1. At her old house / Mulberry Cottage.
2. a) You should have ticked:
   The teacher gave a custody to the child for bad behaviour.
   b) Because custody and custard sound similar.
3. To emphasise how Andy felt. OR
   To make the reader say it with more emphasis.
4. You should have matched these pairs:
   Andy's mum and dad both wanted her to — live in their new houses.
   The counsellor wanted Andy to — play with the dolls.
   Andy wanted to — keep Radish in her pocket.
   Andy did not want to — share the name of her mascot.
5. Your answer should mention three reasons. Examples:
   She thought it was pointless because her mum and dad did not want to be a family anymore.
   She did not want to play with the 'silly old dolls'.
   The counsellor kept trying to talk about Radish, and Andy didn't want to.
   She wanted to keep her problems private.
   The counsellor treated her like a 2-year-old.
6. One of the following phrases:
   'I like to hold her tight when I'm feeling funny.'
   'She's mine and she's private.'

Pages 50 and 51: The Suitcase Kid — Question Set 2

1. Examples: Because she didn't want things to change.
   OR She wanted her family to stay together.
2. Any two of the following occasions. Examples:
   When she doesn't know who to live with.
   When the counsellor takes Radish from her.
   When the counsellor undid Radish's dress
   When she pokes the dolls in the tummy.
3. There are several possible answers to this question. Here are some examples:
   Andy thinks: the counsellor is only pretending to be casual
   Evidence from the text: 'I knew she was trying to suss things out.'
   OR
   Andy thinks: the counsellor is annoying
   Evidence from the text: '…in that silly voice grown-ups always use when they're trying to get you to like them.'
   OR
   Andy thinks: the counsellor is being nosy
   Evidence from the text: '…to let this lady paw at her… in a very rude sort of way.'
4. Example: She doesn't want to share something so personal. She says Radish 'is mine and she is private'.
5. There are several possible answers to this question. Here are some examples:
   The counsellor might think: Andy is feeling very angry about her parents' separation.
   Evidence from the text: 'I poked the mummy doll and the daddy doll in the stomachs.'
   OR
   The counsellor might think: Andy does not want to talk about her feelings.
   Evidence from the text: 'I just shrugged and shook my head.'

Challenge

Example:
I think Andy feels she needs someone on her side who can bring her some luck, as she is worried about what is happening to her family. She may feel lonely and in need of a friend. Radish is more important to her than just a toy.

Text 9 — Playscript

Pages 54 and 55: The Search for Odysseus — Question Set 1

1. You should have ticked:
   a short description to set the scene
   character names to show who's speaking
   character directions within speech
   stage directions between speech
2. Example:
   Athene is trying to convince him that the Cyclops is dangerous so he should be careful. She is warning Telemachus that if the Cyclops knows the truth he will get eaten.

Answers

3. You should have ticked: He smells the sweat of Telemachus.
4. You should have matched these words with their meanings:
   impetuousness — acting without thought or care
   tenfold — ten times as big
   survey — observe
   conviction — confidence
   slay — kill
5. You should have given the events the following numbers:
   Telemachus lies about his father. — 5
   Athene tries to warn Telemachus about the dangers ahead. — 2
   Odysseus blinds the Cyclops during a fight. — 1
   The Cyclops laughs at the thought that Telemachus might harm him. — 4
6. Example:
   He thinks that if he hides, he'll worry too much about what might happen, he'll become really frightened and then he'll lose all his confidence.

Pages 56 and 57: The Search for Odysseus — Question Set 2

1. You should have matched these quotes with their meanings:
   'Your throat is no wider than a reed pipe' — You are so small in comparison to me.
   'your voice no deeper than a song bird' — You are more like a boy than a man.
   'you cannot even lie with conviction' — You do not convince me of your bravery.
2. Any two of the following examples:
   'Of course I'm afraid. He eats people.'
   'If I have time to think I'll be overcome with dread.'
   'we see the giant as a huge blacksmith.'
   'one of his blacksmiths' tools which becomes a weapon.'
   'What friends I had — I had for dinner'
   'He takes a lunge for Telemachus'
3. *Your answer should reflect what's happened in the extract and show how the situation has become more dangerous and risky.*
   Example: I don't think Telemachus will feel like this towards the end of the extract because he has now witnessed the behaviour of the Cyclops. He is threatening Telemachus and making him feel unsafe. He also now has his sword. This kind of adventure and curiosity will most likely lead to danger.
4. He hesitates because he is lying. Odysseus is his father, not his enemy.
5. Example:
   Athene says 'Don't be so ready to tell him who you really are — it gets us into trouble'. This suggests that they have already been in trouble because of Telemachus's honesty.

Challenge

Your answer must be supported with evidence from the text. Example:
I disagree with this statement because I think the Cyclops will know that he is lying like he did before '... you cannot even lie with conviction.' The Cyclops has just picked up the sword that Telemachus has dropped so he could use it against Telemachus because he's angry at being lied to.
OR
I agree with this statement because if he tells the Cyclops that he is the son of the man who blinded him, there's no way he'll get out of the cave alive. The giant has already proven to be angry and violent 'What friends I had — I had for dinner.' He has a blacksmiths' tool in his hand as a weapon and he mentions how unlucky he is not to be able to see.

Acknowledgements

p.10-11: Adapted article © The Sun / News Licensing
p.10-11: Photos © Albanpix
p.16-17: From GREGOR AND THE CURSE OF THE WARMBLOODS by Suzanne Collins. Copyright © 2005 by Suzanne Collins. Reprinted by permission of Scholastic Inc.
p.16: Landscape graphic © LEOcrafts / DigitalVision Vectors / Getty Images
p.17: Foliage graphic © skeeg / DigitalVision Vectors / Getty Images
p.22-23: The Brilliance of Bees by Sharon Keeley-Holden
p.28-29: Adapted extract from Stuff You Should Know by John Farndon and Rob Beattie. Published by QED Publishing, 2015.
p.29: Fridge graphic © MIKKEL JUUL JENSEN / SCIENCE PHOTO LIBRARY
p.34-35: Text copyright ©2010 Atinuke. Illustrations ©2010 Lauren Tobia. WELCOME HOME, ANNA HIBISCUS! by Atinuke & illustrated by Lauren Tobia. Reproduced by permission of Walker Books Ltd, London SE11 5HJ. www.walker.co.uk
p.40-41: Say No to Bullying by Louise Spilsbury. Reproduced by permission of Wayland, an imprint of Hachette Children's Books, Carmelite House, 50 Victoria Embankment, London, EC4Y 0DZ.
p.46-47: From *The Suitcase Kid* by *Jacqueline Wilson*, illustrated by *Nick Sharratt*. Published by *Doubleday*. Reprinted by permission of The Random House Group Limited. © 1992
p.52-53: Reprinted by permission of Aurora Metro Books. 'The Search for Odysseus' by Charles Way Copyright © 2009 Charles Way. For performance rights contact info@aurorametro.com

Pages 3 and 64 contain public sector information licensed under the Open Government Licence v3.0.
http://www.nationalarchives.gov.uk/doc/open-government-licence/version/3/

Images & Clipart throughout the book from Corel ® and Clipart.com

National Curriculum Content Areas

Use the table below to record how pupils are doing in each of the National Curriculum Content Areas.

		2a Word Meaning	2b Retrieval	2c Summarising	2d Inference	2e Prediction	2f Text Meaning	2g Language	2h Comparison
Text 1: Black Beauty	Set 1	Q5	Q1 Q2 Q3 Q4	Q6					
	Set 2	Q1			Q2 Q3 Q5 Ch	Q4			
Text 2: Pheasant's Revolt	Set 1	Q5	Q1 Q2 Q3a Q4	Q6					Q3b
	Set 2	Q3	Q5		Q2 Q4 Ch			Q1	
Text 3: Gregor and the Curse of the Warmbloods	Set 1	Q3	Q1 Q2	Q5				Q4 Q6	
	Set 2		Q1 Q4		Q3 Q5 Ch	Q2a			Q2b
Text 4: The Brilliance of Bees	Set 1	Q4 Q5	Q1 Q2 Q6	Q3					
	Set 2	Q2		Q1 Q5a	Q3 Ch		Q5b	Q4	
Text 5: Refrigerators	Set 1	Q4 Q6b	Q2	Q1 Q3 Q5			Q6a		
	Set 2	Q4		Ch	Q3		Q5	Q1	Q2
Text 6: Welcome Home, Anna Hibiscus!	Set 1		Q1 Q3 Q4 Q6		Q2			Q5	
	Set 2	Q1b Q3		Q5	Q1a Q2 Q4 Ch				
Text 7: Say No to Bullying	Set 1	Q6	Q2 Q3	Q1			Q4 Q5		
	Set 2			Q4	Q3		Q1 Ch	Q2	Q5
Text 8: The Suitcase Kid	Set 1	Q2a	Q1 Q4		Q2b Q5		Q3	Q6	
	Set 2			Q3	Q1 Q4 Q5		Q2 Ch		
Text 9: The Search for Odysseus	Set 1	Q4	Q1 Q3 Q6	Q2 Q5					
	Set 2				Q2 Q4 Q5 Ch			Q1	Q3
Total									